S0-FMH-410

# Walk Beside Me

Joan J. Pinkston

Edited by Larry Carrier

Design by Jon Kopp

**SOUNDFORTH**

© 2005 SoundForth. Greenville, South Carolina 29614.
All rights reserved.

# Contents

# Praise the Lord, Sing Hallelujah!

*Psalm 148*
Adapted by William J. Kirkpatrick

Joan J. Pinkston

Praise the Lord, sing hal - le - lu - jah,

For His Name a - lone is high. And His glo - ry

© 2005 by SoundForth®, Greenville, SC 29614. All rights reserved.
Printed in the U.S.A. Duplication in any form prohibited
without written permission from the publisher.

WARNING: Copying this work without permission is illegal and is NOT COVERED by a CCLI license.

is ex-alt-ed Far a-bove the earth and sky.

unis. *mf*
Praise the Lord, sing hal-le-lu-jah, From the heav-ens praise His name;

Praise the Lord, our great Cre - a - tor, All His an - gels praise pro - claim. All His hosts to - geth - er praise Him, Sun and moon and stars on high; Praise the Lord, O

4

Lyrics:
heav'n of heavens His great glory magnify.

Praise the Lord, sing hallelujah, For His Name alone is high. And His glory is exalted

Far\_\_ a - bove the\_\_ earth and\_\_ sky.

Let the earth sing hal - le - lu - jah, Rag - ing\_\_ seas and

*43* **unis.** *mf*     *div.*

crea - tures all, Fire and hail and snow___ and___ tem - pest,

*46*     Ⓔ *mp with great intensity*

Storm - y___ winds that hear His___ call. Kings of earth and

*with great intensity*
**unis.** *mp*

Ⓔ

*mp with great intensity*

*49*     *mf*

all___ the___ peo - ple, Princ - es great, earth's judg - es___ all

*div.*
*mf*

*mf*

Praise His name, young men and maid - ens,

Ag - ed men and chil - dren small.

F · ff · Majestically

Praise the Lord, sing hal - le - lu - jah,

F · Majestically

For His__ Name a - lone is__ high.

And His glo - ry is ex - alt - ed

Far__ a - bove the earth__ and sky.__

# Tell Me the Story of Jesus

Fanny J. Crosby

John R. Sweney
Arranged by Joan J. Pinkston

*Smoothly, but with forward motion* ♩ = 96

Tell me the sto-ry of Je - sus,

© 2005 by SoundForth®, Greenville, SC 29614. All rights reserved.
Printed in the U.S.A. Duplication in any form prohibited
without written permission from the publisher.

WARNING: Copying this work without permission is illegal and is NOT COVERED by a CCLI license.

div.
Write on my heart ev - 'ry word;
Tell me the sto - ry most
div.
pre - cious,
Sweet - est that ev - er was heard.
B Altos:
p
Ooh
p
Tell how the an - gels, in cho - rus,
Sang as they wel - comed His
B
p

16

*tutti* *mf*

"Glo - ry to God in the high - est!

*Tenors:* *p*

birth,  Ooh

19

Peace and good tid - ings to earth."

*tutti* *mf*

21 Ⓒ *unis.*

Tell me the sto - ry of Je - sus,  Write on my heart ev - 'ry

*unis.*

Ⓒ

word;    Tell   me the sto - ry most pre - cious,____

Sweet - est that ev - er was heard.

Tell   of the cross   where they

nailed Him, Writh - ing in an - guish and pain;

Tell of the grave where they laid Him, Tell how He liv - eth a-

gain. Love in that sto - ry so ten - der,

Clear - er than ev - er I see: Stay, let me weep while you whis - per, Love paid the ran - som for me.

Tell me the sto - ry of Je - sus,

Write on my heart ev-'ry word;

Tell me the sto - ry most pre - cious,_____ Sweet - est that

ev - er was heard._____

*for Slava*

# Walk Beside Me

Duane Nichols

Joan J. Pinkston

**Prayerfully** ♩ = 90

Piano

*mp*

*unis. mp* (A)

S.
A.

Fa - ther, as I bow be - fore Thee Seek - ing

T.
B.

(A)

*p*

guid - ance for the day, May Thy bless - ed Ho - ly

© 2005 by SoundForth®, Greenville, SC 29614. All rights reserved.
Printed in the U.S.A. Duplication in any form prohibited
without written permission from the publisher.

WARNING: Copying this work without permission is illegal and is NOT COVERED by a CCLI license.

Spir - it Be the Guar - dian of my way._____ Walk be -

side me lest I fal - ter; Walk be - side me lest I

Walk be - side me

stray. In Thy love and ten - der mer - cy Guide these

lest I stray,

fee - ble feet of clay.

Qui - et - ly I wait be-

*unis.* **mp**

fore Thee, Lis-t'ning to Thy still small voice;

*28*

May I grow in grace and know - ledge, May in Thee my heart re-

*div.*

*31*

*unis. mf*

ⒹWalk be - side me lest I fal - ter, Walk be -

*unis. mf*

joice. Walk be-side me lest I fal - ter,

Ⓓ

*34*

*div.*

*, f*

side me lest I stray. In Thy love and ten - der

*mf*

*div.*

*, f*

Walk be - side me lest I stray.

*mf*

*f*

mer - cy    Guide these fee - ble feet of clay.

Though the shad-ows loom be - fore me, When the dark - ness gath - ers

Lyrics:
near, Safe - ly rest-ing in Thy pres - ence Nev - er

will I doubt or fear. Walk be - side me lest I
Walk be - side me

fal - ter, Walk be - side me lest I stray, In Thy
lest I fal - ter, Walk be - side me lest I stray,

love and ten - der mer - cy Guide these fee - ble feet of

clay. Guide these fee - ble

Guide these fee - ble

feet of clay.

*dedicated to the BJU Musical Mission Team*

# Send the Light

Charles H. Gabriel

Charles H. Gabriel
Arranged by Joan J. Pinkston

© 2005 by SoundForth®, Greenville, SC 29614. All rights reserved.
Printed in the U.S.A. Duplication in any form prohibited
without written permission from the publisher.

WARNING: Copying this work without permission is illegal and is NOT COVERED by a CCLI license.

A

*div.*

call comes ring-ing o'er the rest - less wave, "Send the light! Send the

A

light!" There are souls to res-cue, there are souls to save, Send the

*unis.* *div.*

light! Send the light! Send the

*mf*

15
B
light! the bless-ed gos - pel light; Let it shine from shore to
mf
Send the light! Send the light! Let it shine
B
mf
18
shore! Send the light! the bless-ed gos - pel light; Let it
shore to shore! Send the light! Send the light!
21
mp
shine for - ev - er - more.
8
mp
Let it shine for - ev - er - more.
mp

Let us pray that grace may ev-'ry- where a-bound; Send the light! Send the light! And a

33
Christ-like spir-it ev-'ry-where be found, Send the light! Send the
36
D
light!
Send the light! the bless-ed gos-pel light;
Send the light! the bless-ed gos-pel light; Let it
D
39
Let it shine from shore to shore! Send the light! the bless-ed
shine from shore to shore! Send the light! the bless-ed

28

crown a - bove, Send the light! Send the light!

*poco rit. div.* **f** Ⓕ *a tempo*

Send the light!_____ the bless-ed gos - pel light; Let it

shine_____ from shore to shore! Send the light!_____ the bless-ed gos - pel light;_____ Let it shine, let it

Let it shine,

shine for - ev - er - more. Send the

light!_____

*dedicated to Greg and Sue Ann Phillips*

# Christ for Me

Richard Jukes

Joan J. Pinkston

Lyrics under the staves:

My heart is trust - ing Thee, O God,___ Trust-ing Thee, trust-ing Thee, And my im -

© 1996 by Faith Free Presbyterian Church, Greenville, SC 29615.
All rights reserved. Used by permission.

WARNING: Copying this work without permission is illegal and is NOT COVERED by a CCLI license.

13
mor - tal choice is made: Christ for me! Christ for
16
mf
B
me! He is my Proph - et, Priest and King, Who did for
mf
19
div.
me sal - va - tion bring; And while I've breath my lips shall
div.

sing: Christ for me! Christ for me!

*unis.* *mp*

In Him I

*unis.* *mp*

*mp*

see the God-head shine;_____ Christ for me! Christ for

me! He is the maj - es - ty di - vine;_____ Christ for

me! Christ for me! The Fa-ther's well - be-lov - ed

Son,_____ Co-part-ner of His roy-al throne,_____ Who did for hu - man guilt a - tone; Christ for me! Christ for

me!

Let oth-ers

52
E
boast of heaps of gold; Christ for me! Christ for
E
55
me! His rich - es nev - er can be told; Christ for
58
div. f
me! Christ for me! Their gold will
div. f
f

waste and wear a - way;_____ Their hon - ors per - ish in a

day,_____ My por - tion nev - - er can de - cay:

Christ for

Christ for me! Christ for me! Christ for me!_____

Christ for me!_____

me!_____

# Ho! Ye That Thirst

*Scottish Psalter, 1880*
Paraphrase of Isaiah 55

Traditional English Melody
Arranged by Joan J. Pinkston

*Joyfully* ♩ = 120

Piano

*mf*

S.
A.

unis. *mp* Ⓐ

*mp* Ⓐ

Ho! ye that thirst, ap-proach the spring Where

liv-ing wa-ters flow: Free to that sa-cred

unis. *mp*

T.
B.

© 2005 by SoundForth®, Greenville, SC 29614. All rights reserved.
Printed in the U.S.A. Duplication in any form prohibited
without written permission from the publisher.

WARNING: Copying this work without permission is illegal and is NOT COVERED by a CCLI license.

foun - tain___ all With - out a___ price may go. How___

long to streams of___ false___ de - lights Will ye in crowds re -

pair? How___ long___ your___ strength and sub - stance___ waste On tri - fles___ light as air?

Seek

Seek while His ear Is___ o - pen to your

ye the Lord while yet___ His___ ear Is o - pen___ to your

call; While mercy is near, Be-

call; While of-fered mer-cy still__ is__ near, Be-

fore__ His__ foot-stool fall. Let__ sin-ners quit__ their__

e-vil__ ways, Their e-vil tho'ts for-go, And

To Him__ re - turn, Re - turn - ing grace will

God, when they to Him__ re - turn, Re - turn - ing__ grace will

show.

With joy and peace shall

then__ be__ led The glad con - vert - ed lands; The

loft - y moun - tains then__ shall__ sing, The for - ests__ clap their

hands. Where__ bri - ars grew__ 'midst bar - ren__ wilds, Shall__

*div. f*

*f*

firs and myr - tles spring;_____ And na - ture, through its

ut - most___ bounds,_____ E -

E - ter - nal___ praise,

ter - nal___ praise, E - ter - nal___ praise shall sing!_____

# I Will Praise Him

Margaret J. Harris

Joan J. Pinkston

© 2005 by SoundForth®, Greenville, SC 29614. All rights reserved.
Printed in the U.S.A. Duplication in any form prohibited
without written permission from the publisher.

WARNING: Copying this work without permission is illegal and is NOT COVERED by a CCLI license.

sin, I o-beyed _____ the Spir-it's woo - ing, When He

said, Wilt thou__ be clean? I will praise Him! I will

praise__ Him!_____ Praise the Lamb for sin-ners slain;_____ Give Him glo - ry, all ye peo - ple, For His blood can cleanse__ each

stain.                                                Since the

Since the way_____ is straight and nar - row,_____

way_____ is straight and nar - row,     All I

All I claimed _____ was swept a - way,

claimed _____ was swept a - way; My am -

My am-bi - tions, plans and wish-es, _____ At my feet in

bi - tions, plans and wish - es, At my feet in ash - es

ash - es lay. I will praise Him! I will praise Him! _____ Praise the

lay.

Lamb for sin - ners slain;_____ Give Him glo - ry, all ye

peo - ple, For His blood can cleanse__ each stain.

Bless-ed be_____ the name of

**40**

Je - sus! I'm so glad_____ He took__ me in; He's for-

**43**

_div._

giv - en my trans - gres - sions, He has cleansed my heart from

_div._

**46**

sin. I will praise Him! I will praise__ Him!_____ Praise the

Lamb for sin - ners slain;_____ Give Him glo - ry, all ye peo - ple, For His blood can cleanse each stain. For His blood can cleanse each stain!_____

For His blood can cleanse,_

# Day by Day

Carolina V. Sandell-Berg
Translated by Andrew L. Skoog

Oskar Ahnfelt
Arranged by Joan J. Pinkston

Day by day and with each pass-ing mo - ment, Strength I

find to meet my tri - als here; Trust-ing in my Fa-ther's wise be-

© 2005 by SoundForth®, Greenville, SC 29614. All rights reserved.
Printed in the U.S.A. Duplication in any form prohibited
without written permission from the publisher.

WARNING: Copying this work without permission is illegal and is NOT COVERED by a CCLI license.

stow-ment, I've no cause for wor-ry or for fear. He whose

heart is kind be-yond all meas-ure Gives un-to each day what He deems

best, Lov-ing-ly its part of pain and pleas-ure, Min-gling

toil with peace__ and__ rest.

*unis.* ***mf***   Ⓒ

Ev-'ry day the Lord Him-self is

near me With a spec - ial mer - cy for each hour; All my

28

cares He fain would bear and cheer me, He whose name is Coun-sel-lor and

31 *div.* **f** Ⓓ

Pow'r. The pro - tec - tion of His child and treas - ure Is a

*div.* **f**

**f**

34 *unis.* **mp**

charge that on Him - self He laid; "As thy

*unis.* **mp**

days, thy strength shall be in meas - ure," This the pledge to me___ He___

made.

Help me then in ev - 'ry trib - u - la - tion So to

trust Thy prom-is-es, O Lord, That I lose not faith's sweet con-so-

la - tion Of-fered me with - in Thy ho - ly

with - in Thy

*poco rit.* *f* (F) *a tempo*

Word. Help me, Lord, when toil and trou-ble meet-ing; E'er to

58

take, as from a fa-ther's hand, One by one, the days, the mo-ments

fleet - ing, Till I reach the prom - ised__ land.

Till I reach the prom - ised__ land._____

# Index